NORTH POLE

A 'WEE' BIT DESPERATE

SCREEEECH TO HALT!

Printed and Published in Great Britain by D. C. Thomson & Co., Ltd., 185 Fleet Street, London EC4A 2HS.
© D. C. Thomson & Co. Ltd., 2001.

ISBN 0-85116-778-0

D0480488

£6.10

WHY DID THE FOOTBALLER WEAR FLIPPERS?

BECAUSE HE WAS IN THE FIRST TEAM POOL!

ORCHESTRATED RIOT

THE VISITING MUSIC TEACHER IS COMING TO SCHOOL!

BASH STREET SCHOOL

MUSIC TEACHER

PARP

RUMBLE

In class IIB.

I'M GOING TO LET YOU ALL TRY OUT VARIOUS INSTRUMENTS — TO SEE WHAT YOU'RE GOOD AT!

MUSICAL INSTRUMENTS

PULL

TRUNDLE

OH! NOT NOW!

WAA!

PARP!

PYDNNG

I'D QUITE LIKE TO PLAY THIS!

BUT I'M NOT SURE IF MY MOUTH IS BIG ENOUGH!

MAYBE NOT — BUT YOU'VE GOT A VERY USEFUL HARD HEAD!

...YOU ARE DISTURBING DANNY'S DRUMMING!

WAP

THUNK

WHAT A WONDERFUL SOUND YOU ARE GETTING FROM THAT BIG DRUM!

OO... BAH... DOOM!

Then —

RIP OPEN

HEH-HEH! IT WAS CUTHBERT INSIDE IT!

WE GIVE UP! NONE OF THESE INSTRUMENTS AR AT ALL SUITED TO YOU LOT!

WOW! MY HEAD!

DAZED

WHAT DO YOU GET IF YOU CROSS A DOG WITH A PHONE?

A GOLDEN RECEIVER!

OOH!

WAH!

COO!

DIVE

LEAP

MUSICAL INSTRUMENTS

EH? WHAT'S ALL THIS?

WE BOTH WANT TO PLAY THIS TROMBONE!

PULL

TUG

YEAH!

HOW NICE! THEY'RE BOTH PLAYING IT!

PARP

BADOING

WHACK

I WANT TO PLAY THIS! ALL THE BLACK KEYS ARE MADE OF LIQUORICE!

CHEW

↑ KEYBOARD

AND YOU DON'T REALLY NEED THEM TO PLAY IT!

SCOOP

But—

DON'T SPIT THESE OUT . . .

PING

PHOO

BAH! NOT MADE OF LIQUORICE AFTER ALL! HUH!

YES! I AGREE!

BUT WE MIGHT BE ABLE TO USE THESE!

HOW INTERESTING!

THIS IS SOMEWHERE SAFE TO HAVE OUR CUP OF TEA!

SQUASH

ZAP

TWANG

BOUNCE

CLUNK

FLATTEN

WHAT DO YOU GET IF YOU CROSS A MIDGET WITH DRACULA?

TEETHMARKS IN YOUR KNEES!

OKAY, PLUG! THAT'S A LONG ENOUGH RUN UP, I'D SAY!

WHEEE LEAP

WOW! WHAT A JUMP!

CLANK

HMM! IT DOESN'T COUNT!

PLUG DIDN'T LAND IN THE SAND!

CHIP

CLANK

HAR-HAR! GREAT PRACTISE FOR BUNKER SHOTS!

THERE IT GOES!

OO...WAH! GOOD THROW, FATTY!

PRANG

I'M GOING TO TOSS THIS!

WHIRRRRR

THAT'S IT, SMIFFY! WHEN ARE YOU GOING TO LET IT GO?

What's this? A trial for the Tug O' War?

NOPE!

NNNGH!

TEACHER WAS GOING TO TAKE US TO THE SPORTS GROUND — BUT HIS OLD CAR HAS BROKEN DOWN!

HEH-HEH!

RATTLE

THAT'S IT! PULL IT OVER TO THE SPORTS GROUND — A COUPLE OF PAGES ON!

DOCTOR! DOCTOR! I THINK I'M AN AEROPLANE!

COME DOWN TO EARTH, MAN!

ONE TEACHER AND HIS DOG

At 9 a.m.

THIS IS A MAGIC BELL, READERS! ALL I HAVE TO DO IS RING IT...

YAHOO!
GOAL!
KICK!
THE
BALL
WATCH
OUT

...AND IT MAKES KIDS DISAPPEAR!

DING

WAA!

TIME TO GO!

ZOOM

SUPER JOB! THEY'RE ALL ROUNDED UP!

WOOF! WOOF!

HUMPH! SHOW OFF!

NOT REALLY! HE'S JUST A VERY SMART DOG!

GOOD! IF THIS DOG'S SO SMART — HE'LL KNOW HOW TO PLAY...

TUG

After playtime —

HMM! TOOTS IS MISSING!

WOOF!

I WONDER WHERE SHE'S HIDING.

SNIFF SNIFF

WOW! HE MUST BE OFF ON HER TRAIL.

ZOOM

HAS HE FOUND HER IN HERE.

WHAT DO YOU GET IF YOU CROSS A SKUNK WITH A HOMING PIGEON?

A BAD SMELL THAT WON'T GO AWAY.

BUT I NOW HAVE A WAY TO BRING THEM ALL BACK!

PHEEEP!

SCHOOL

ZOOM

WOOF! WOOF!

WOOF! WOOF!

WAA!

HA-HA! A SHEEPDOG!

ER . . .

OO . . . ER!

. . . FETCH!

THROW

WHEN HE GOES FOR THE STICK — WE'LL RUSH OUT OF THE DOOR!

But—

SHUT FAST

DROOL! THERE'S A BIT OF LOLLY LEFT ON THIS STICK!

HE'S ALSO SMART ENOUGH TO FIT A PADLOCK ON THE DOOR! HA-HA-HA!

D-I-Y BOOK

WOOF!

Later, at playtime.

KITCHEN WINDOW

PUSH

IN YOU GO, TOOTS! I HOPE THIS PLAN TO GET RID OF THE SHEEPDOG WORKS!

SCHOOL KITCHEN

ZOOM

In the kitchen.

OUR PLAN TO FILL THE DOG FULL OF TOOTS' SUPER SHEPHERD'S PIE HAS WORKED BETTER THAN WE'D HOPED . . .

. . . TEACHER AND THE HEAD ARE TUCKING INTO THE SHEPHERD'S PIE TOO! HA-HA! NO ONE TO TEACH OR CHASE US NOW!

YUM! MUNCH! MAKES A CHANGE FROM OLIVE'S FOUL FODDER!

CHOMP!

MUNCH! THIS IS MY THIRD HELPING!

Fun at Your Convenience

LES ENFANTS TERRIBLES

HERE ARE THE RESULTS OF THE FRENCH TEST!

TITTER! TOO EASY!

CUTHBERT-CLASS SWOT

FRENCH TEST

FULL MARKS TO YOU, PLUG! ONLY ONE IN CLASS!

SWOON

PLUG 100%

OOO . . . OH!

LET'S ROLL OUT THE RED CARPET! LAY ON A SPECIAL FRENCH STYLE LUNCH FOR HER!

FROGS' LEGS MAYBE? YEUCH!

CLASS IIB

In Olive's kitchen —

I'LL MAKE A SPECIAL 'FRENCH SOUP'! THEY'RE KEEN ON SOUP IN FRANCE!

SPLENDID!

KITCHEN

STIR

STIR

Later —

YOU LOT CAN TRY MY 'FRENCH STYLE' SOUP FIRST!

CRASH

LOOK HERE, OLIVE . . . WE CAN'T . . .

THERE'S A FRENCH GIRL HERE TO SEE PLUG!

DINING HALL

DINING HALL

AHA! PLUG!

FIFI?

LET ME KISS YOU ON BOTH CHEEKS, PLUG!

WOW! FLEE!

TOUGH LUCK, PLUG!

PUCKER

BUT . . . HOW ARE YOU SO GOOD AT FRENCH, PLUG?

HA-HA! EASY . . .

SMELLING SALTS

. . . I HAVE A FRENCH PEN PAL — FIFI!

FRENCH POSTCARD

SHE'S COMING OVER FROM FRANCE TO VISIT BASH STREET! FIFI ARRIVES TODAY!

WONDERFUL!

AHA! FRENCH ONIONS!

YUM! FRENCH BREAD!

EH! A FRENCH BERET?

YEUCH! AN ONION SELLER'S BIKE!

OUI! TO GIVE IT FLAVOUR! CHUCKLE!

AH, PLUG! SCHLURP!

HEH-HEH!

ER . . . I DIDN'T WANT TO PUT FIFI OFF WRITING TO ME, SO WHEN SHE ASKED FOR A PHOTO — I SENT ONE OF DANNY!

SLURP SLURP

OO-LA-LA! YOU ARE EVEN MORE HANDSOME IN ZE FLESH, PLUG!

ZOOM

WHAT'S GREEN AND GOES CAMPING?

A BRUSSEL'S SCOUT!

WEATHER STATION MASTERS

COME ON, TEACHER. WE'RE READY FOR OUR CLASS OUTING!

HMM! WILL IT STAY FAIR? RAIN? SNOW? HMM!

Soon —

OKAY! LET'S GO ON OUR VISIT TO THE BEANOTOWN WEATHER STATION!

HEH-HEH!

WAVES BEAM IN AND ARE PICKED UP ON THE DISH TO SHOW UP ON THIS SCREEN!

SATELLITE DISH

. . . MORE OVER HERE TOO . . .

TWIST HIS LEG OFF!

PUNCH HIM!

EH? WHERE ARE THE KIDS?

BZZT! TING! DING!

WILL IT BE DRY AT, 13 TEACHER'S LANE, BEANOTOWN, TODAY?

TAP! TAP!

WAIT A FEW MOMENTS FOR AN ANSWER!

SNIFF! I SMELL FOOD IN THERE! SNIFF!

BZZT! TING! DING!

SNIFF! SNIFF!

BZZT! TING! DING!

COMPUTER SIDE DOOR

PUSH!

SNIFF! SNIFF!

BZZT! BLEEP

WHY DID THE BANANA GO TO HOSPITAL?

BECAUSE IT WASN'T PEELING WELL!

TEACHER'S TAKING NO CHANCES WITH THE WEATHER TODAY!

JUST AS WELL I HAD AN UMBRELLA, EH? HAW-HAW!

SPLOOSH!

SPLOOSH!

AW!

At the Weather Station —

BEHAVE IN HERE! LOTS OF HI-TEC EXPENSIVE COMPUTERS AROUND!

PONK!

I'LL SHOW YOU WHERE WE GET SATELLITE PICTURES OF WEATHER CLOUDS FROM ALL AROUND THE WORLD!

FLATTEN HIS NOSE!

LIVE FROM OUTBACK AUSTRALIA

YAHOO!

HO-HO! WRESTLING ON SATELLITE!

THIS HI-TEC COMPUTER CAN FORECAST WEATHER FOR ANYWHERE IN THE WORLD. SOMEONE CARE TO TEST IT?

BZZT!

TING!

DING!

BLEEP!

ER . . . THIS IS MRS TEACHER'S WASHDAY. CAN I ASK IF IT'LL BE DRY FOR HER HANGING OUT THE CLOTHES?

DING!

TING!

BZZT!

BLEEP!

OK!

CHOMP! CHOMP! I KNOW HOW IT WORKS, TEACHER!

FATTY'S INSIDE THE COMPUTER!

HA-HA! THE CAPTAIN IN HERE CHECKS THE HANGING SEAWEED TO TELL IF IT'LL RAIN OR NOT BUT AS A DOUBLE CHECK HE KNOWS IF HIS CORNS ARE SORE IT'LL RAIN!

HO-HO!

HEH-HEH!

HUH! SOME HI-TEC COMPUTER!

WAVE!

OH, NO! RUINED! OUR INTERNATIONAL REPUTATION IS IN TATTERS! SOB! WAA!

CHORTLE! THE OLD WAYS ARE THE BEST!

BYEE!

NAME ME THREE ANIMALS THAT LIVE IN CHINA.

THREE PANDAS!

TESTING! TESTING!

TOMORROW WE SHALL HAVE A CLASS TEST TO FIND OUT WHO IS THE SMARTEST PUPIL. THAT PUPIL CAN THEN SIT HERE, AT THE 'PRIZE PUPIL'S' DESK!

PAT! PAT!

Cuthbert, the class swot!

SMUG

PRIZE PUPIL

PRIZE PUPIL

I HAVE A GOOD IDEA WHO THAT PUPIL WILL BE!

TITTER!

HUMPH!

RESERVED FOR CUTHBERT

HO-HO! BRAINS OVER BRAWN!

HUMPH! OUTSMARTED FATTY!

CARROT! DROOL! CARROT!

ZOOM!

CARE TO TRY OUT OUR NEW VIDEO GAMES, CUTHBERT?

OKAY!

CHORTLE! IT'LL TAKE HIM ALL NIGHT TO TRY THESE OUT. HE'LL BE TOO SLEEPY FOR THE TEST TOMORROW.

NO NEED TO LEAVE THEM . . .

. . . I'LL TRY THEM ALL OUT NOW!

HMM!

EH? WHAT'S HE DOING?

I'VE WRITTEN A FEW SONGS FOR YOU CATS TO SING. THEY'LL SOUND MUCH BETTER THAN YOUR WAILINGS!

CATS

CATS

CATS

WAVE!

CATS

CATS

AH! MUCH, MUCH BETTER.

Next day —

HUH! WE'RE FED-UP OF CUTHBERT BEING THE TOP PUPIL!

I HAVE A CLEVER, CRAFTY AND BRILLIANT PLAN TO FIX HIM . . .

SKIP!

. . . I'LL THUMP CUTHBERT!

HO-HO! WAIT FOR IT!

But —

SILENCE

EH? VERY QUIET!

WOW!

DINGO! BZZZT!

DONG!

Soon —

GASP! TOP SCORE!

THE NEW CHAMP!

HOT SHOT!

TOO EASY!

WIPE!

So later, at Cuthbert's house.

I MUST GET AN EARLY NIGHT, REST MY SUPER BRAIN FOR THE TEST TOMORROW.

HUMPH! WE'LL HAVE TO KEEP HIM AWAKE.

That night —

WAIL! HOWL! WAA!

OO . . . AWFUL DIN! I'LL HAVE TO DO SOMETHING.

Kids in disguise.

YAWN! YAWN!

IT WORKED! A LATE NIGHT FOR CUTHBERT WILL STOP HIM BEATING US IN THE TEST.

HEH-HEH!

THEIR PLAN DIDN'T WORK!

ZZZZZ!

EVEN FAST ASLEEP, CUTHBERT'S BRIGHTER THAN THE REST. HO-HO!

HMMMPH!

SNARL!

ONE PLUS ONE . . .

. . . ZZZ!

PRIZE PUPIL

CUTHBERT
5 x 6 = 30

WRITE

PRIZE

HOW DOES A GHOST COOK EGGS?

IT TERRIFRIES THEM!

DODGY BUSINESS

I'D BETTER PREPARE MYSELF FOR THE USUAL MORNING BATTLE!

CLASS IIB

WOW! THEY'VE FOUND BOOKS THEY ENJOY READING!

So—

I'LL PUT MY PET MOUSE HERE!

SQUEAK
SQUEAK

LEAP

LOOK! THAT BOY WITH THE METAL DETECTOR HAS FOUND TREASURE!

Two passing workmen.

SQUEAK
SQUEAK

CRASH

NOW WE'LL TIME THEM!

POOR CUTHBERT HAS BEEN BURIED UNDER ALL OF THIS!

PHEW! ONLY A TRICK — THERE'S CUTHBERT!

MUMBLE!

I'M CONFISCATING THESE DODGE BOOKS — THEY CAUSE TOO MUCH TROUBLE!

GRAB

FL

WHY WAS THE EGYPTIAN CONFUSED?

BECAUSE HIS DADDY WAS A MUMMY!

I'VE LET THEM HAVE A READ OF MY DODGE BOOKS!

101 DODGES

HMM! ROGER!

I'M GOING TO TAKE ADVANTAGE OF THIS PEACE AND QUIET TO DO SOME TEACHING!

SKIP

IF IT TAKES ONE MAN TWO HOURS TO DIG A HOLE 2 METRES WIDE BY 2 METRES LONG BY 4 METRES DEEP, HOW LONG WILL IT TAKE TWO MEN TO DIG THE SAME SIZE OF HOLE?

NO NEED TO WORK IT OUT — WE'LL USE ONE OF ROGER'S DODGES!

YEAH!

BAH! NOTHING THERE AT ALL!

IT TOOK THOSE MEN TWO MINUTES, TEACHER!

WAH! YOU LOT HAD BETTER GET THAT HOLE FILLED IN BEFORE THE HEAD SEES IT!

THUD
THUD

USE THIS DODGE!

101 DODGES

Soon—

EH?

HMM! MAYBE I COULD USE A DODGE!

I'LL REVERSE THE BATTERY IN THIS BATTERY OPERATED CLOCK!

CLICK CLICK

AND IT WILL RUN BACKWARDS!

WHIRR

AH! SO IT'LL SOON BE BACK IN TIME WHEN I WAS IN BED AND NONE OF THIS HAD EVER HAPPENED!

SNEAK AWAY

SNORE

GRUNT

101 DODGES

LAUGHTER A FASHION

HUH! WHAT A SCRUFFY BUNCH! BAD IMAGE FOR THE SCHOOL, TEACHER!

YES, YOUR HEADSHIP!

So—

I'VE ASKED MISTER JAY CLOTH, A TOP FASHION DESIGNER, TO MAKE SOME BASH STREET OUTFITS!

HEAD'S STUDY

SEWING MACHINE

GOOD IDEA

OO! CAN I MODEL MY NEW OUTFIT WHEN IT'S READY? I'D LOVE TO BE A MODEL ON THE CATWALK!

WHAT? YOU?

WAGGLE

TIPTOE

CHORTLE! HA-HA! NO CHANCE! HEH HEH!

RAGE

OH, NO! YOU SHOULDN'T HAVE SAID THAT, MISTER!

SQUEAL! OW!

THUMP

WALLOP

KICK

THIS MAKES YOU LOOK MUCH THINNER, FATTY! HO-HO!

SQUEAL!

TUG

BUT WHERE'S TEACHER?

ER . . . TEACHER'S IN HERE — TRYING ON HIS NEW OUTFIT!

CUP-BOARD

OO!

CUP-BOARD

EH?

WHAT DO YOU GET IF YOU CROSS A CLOCK WITH A SCOTSMAN?

A CUCKOO JOCK!

I MUST MEET THE CHILDREN BEFORE I CAN CREATE OUTFITS TO BRING OUT EACH OF THEIR TALENTS!

TALENTS? TITTER!

CLASS IIB

SEWING MACHINE

INK

TWANG

DUCK PLOP

THUMP

CHORTLE!

YAHOO!

HMM! I'LL MAKE A FEW NOTES!

THUD

One thumping later—

OOH! WELL, PERHAPS YOU COULD BE A SUPER MODEL, TOOTS!

HUH!

Later—

YOUR OUTFITS ARE READY!

HERE'S YOUR, PLUG! A NICE BIG HOOD TO HIDE YOUR UGLY MUSH!

ZIP

TEACHER! TEACHER! COME OUT!

NO! GO AWAY! TAKE THE REST OF THE DAY OFF! GO AWAY!

CUP-BOARD

THUD THUMP THUD

Only you readers are being allowed to see Teacher's newly designed outfit. Oo! Isn't it lovely?

Jaunty new mortar-board.

CLEAR OFF! I'M NOT COMING OUT!

Pockets for chalk, paper-clips etc.

AW! LET'S SEE YOUR OUTFIT, TEACHER!

THUD

End of term REPORT

ART CLASS PROVED POPULAR THIS TERM.

APART FROM THE DAY A SPIDER DROPPED DOWN SPOTTY'S NECK!

AND EVERYONE WAS SPOTTY FOR A DAY.

THE BASH STREET KIDS are CASTAWAYS

I'VE HAD A LETTER ABOUT YOU LOT.

WASN'T US!

WE WERE SOMEWHERE ELSE.

I WAS ON HOLIDAY AT THE TIME.

IT'S FROM A TV COMPANY.

REALLY?

THEY WANT TO USE YOU LOT IN A TELEVISION PROGRAMME . . .

YOU DON'T SAY!

IT'S NO USE — WE'LL NEVER GET THIS OVER THE WALL.

NO SLACKING!

PUSH

WITH MY BRAINPOWER THIS WILL BE A PIECE OF CAKE.

LIFT

BLAM

GET THE BARREL OVER THE NET WITHOUT IT TOUCHING THE GROUND.

ROLL

PHEW! PASS IT ON.

ZOOM!

I CAN HELP AGAIN.

SAS

Much torture later —

GOOD SHOW! NOW I WANT YOU TO BUILD A RAFT AND CROSS THE LAKE.

NO PROBS!

SPLOT!

THIS'LL TAKE AGES.

NO, IT WON'T.

JUG

PLUG'S EARS MAKE GREAT PROPELLERS.

SPIN!

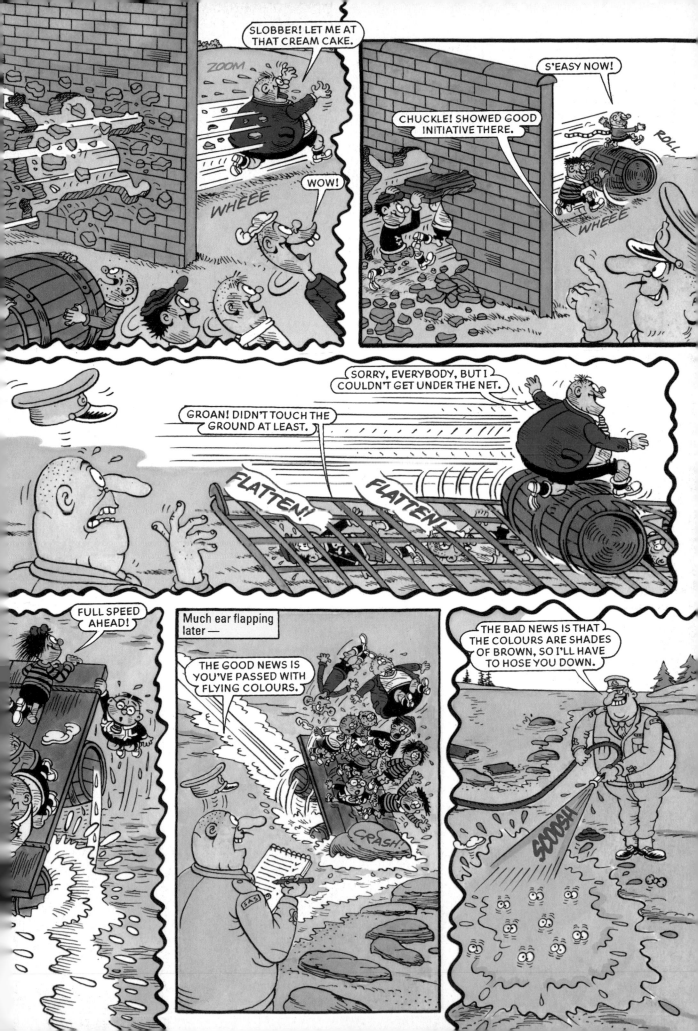

WHEN YOU GO TO THE ISLAND YOU CAN TAKE ONE LUXURY ITEM WITH YOU.

I'LL TAKE THIS COS I MUST TAKE CARE OF MY GOOD LOOKS.

YOU NEED IT. PUT PLENTY ON, PLUG.

PUSH

SPLATCH!

FIZZOG FACE CREAM

GLOOP!

I'LL BRING MY EMERGENCY FLARES.

WHY DON'T YOU BRING A BRAIN, SMIFFY?

I'LL TAKE A MATHS BOOK — TO LIGHT THE FIRE.

NO! NO! YOU FIEND!

MATH BOOK

I'M TAKING A TREE TO GROW APPLES FOR MY BELOVED TEACHER.

HISS! BOO!

APPLE TREE

THIS HAT WILL KEEP THE FLIES AWAY.

HA-HA! IT'LL KEEP EVERYTHING AWAY!

CHEEK!

I'LL TAKE MY HOME-MADE WIND-POWERED MICROWAVE OVEN.

SPIN

SPIN

In the helicopter —

LEND ME YOUR TREE, CUTHBERT.

WHY?

SNATCH

KERRASH!

SO I CAN GIVE IT TO PLUG.

PRANG!

FLAP. WHIRR-FL...

PLUGS EARS HAVE MANY USES!

OH — — NO!

WHAT A LOVELY SURPRISE, EH? I WAS FLOWN OUT EARLIER.

B-BASH STREET SCHOOL!

AND TEACHER!

SCHOOL

DIVE

YOU LOT ARE MORE THAN ENOUGH FOR ME. I'M OFF HOME.

BYEE!

U.K. 1000 MILES

Soon —

BRR! IT'S NOT SO WARM HERE.

AND THERE'S NO WAY WE'RE SLEEPING IN SCHOOL.

COLD BREEZE

HOI, WHAT ARE OUR WHALE FRIENDS LAUGHING A...

HERE WE ARE, KIDS. YOUR HOME FOR THE NEXT YEAR.

FANTASTIC! MILES AWAY FROM SMELLY OLD SCHOOL.

THERE IS JUST ONE SPECIALLY MADE BUILDING. SEE YOU NEXT YEAR.

LET'S EXPLORE!

PADDLE

TELL ME WHAT ELSE YOU MIGHT FIND ON AN ISLAND SEASHORE?

COCKLES
MUSSELS
SEAWEED

AN OLD CRAB LIKE HIM.

HEH-HEH!

LOOK, SIR — I'VE SPOTTED ANOTHER SCHOOL.

A SCHOOL OF WHALES, THAT IS.

NIGHTMARE!

THE BASH STREET WHALES.

HO — HO — HO!

I'LL HAVE A LOOK THROUGH MY TELESCOPE.

IT'S A BEANO IN A BOTTLE.

I ARRANGED TO HAVE IT DELIVERED EVERY WEEK.

GOOD THINKING, TOOTS!

WHAT HAPPENED NEXT?

Find out on page 81

WHAT'S ROUND AND DANGEROUS?

A VICIOUS CIRCLE!

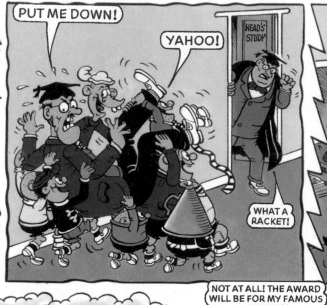

PUT ME DOWN!

YAHOO!

TRING!

WHAT A RACKET!

NOT AT ALL! THE AWARD WILL BE FOR MY FAMOUS COOKING!

GET BACK TO CLASS!

AW!

ERK!

NO! NO! THE AWARD WILL BE FOR ME HAVING TAUGHT THE PUPILS THE ART OF WOODWORK!

SPLAT!

SPLAT!

TWANG!

TWANG!

HO-HO! WE DON'T THINK SO, TEACHER!

WE AWARD THE JANITOR'S CAT WITH THE GOLDEN BRUSH FOR KEEPING THE PLAYGROUND TIDY DESPITE THE MESSY KIDS!

PUSH!

WHUMP!

AHA! THE PIE I LOST LAST YEAR!

GASP!

OO-ER!

OOF!

BOW!

OW!

COO!

WHAT DO CATS USE TO FRESHEN THEIR BREATH?

MOUSEWASH!

YOUR TELEPHONE IS RINGING, HEADMASTER!

HEAD'S STUDY

BLAST!

YES...SCHOOL... AWARD...THIS... AFTERNOON...OKAY...

HEAD'S STUDY

YAHOO!

YELL!

SOMEONE'S COMING TO PRESENT AN AWARD TODAY! I COULDN'T HEAR WHO'S RECEIVING THE REWARD, BUT IT WILL PROBABLY BE ME FOR GIVING THE PUPILS A "DIRECTION" IN LIFE!

CLASS IIB

THWAD!

KITCHEN

DON'T YOU WANT MORE OF MY FRIED CUSTARD AND CHEESE PUDDINGS?

BLECH!

TOPPLE!

FAINT!

TEA

TEA

YES — MY COOKING IS LEGENDARY!

Then —

EEK! OUR VISITORS ARE HERE!

SCREECH!

ROLL OUT THE RED CARPET!

WOW!

GASP!

YAHOO!

SWOON!

OH, NO!

HURRAH!

THE JANITOR VERY KINDLY LET ME TRY OUT MY AWARD!

WHAT GOES DOT-DASH-DOT-DASH-NEIGH?

HORSE CODE!

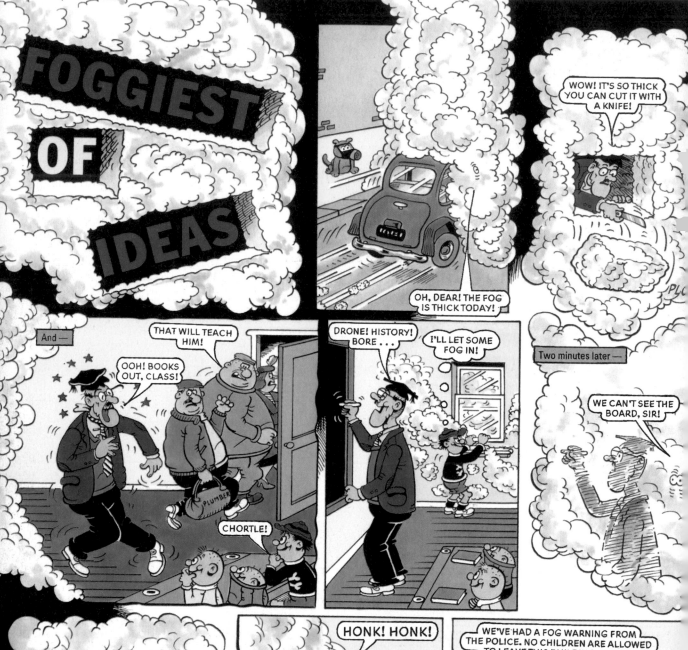

FOGGIEST OF IDEAS

WOW! IT'S SO THICK YOU CAN CUT IT WITH A KNIFE!

OH, DEAR! THE FOG IS THICK TODAY!

And —

OOH! BOOKS OUT, CLASS!

THAT WILL TEACH HIM!

CHORTLE!

DRONE! HISTORY! BORE . . .

I'LL LET SOME FOG IN!

Two minutes later —

WE CAN'T SEE THE BOARD, SIR!

OUCH!

THUD!

OOF! LOOK OUT, YOU OAF!

HONK! HONK!

SIGH! IT'S ONLY HEAD BLOWING HIS NOSE!

WE'VE HAD A FOG WARNING FROM THE POLICE. NO CHILDREN ARE ALLOWED TO LEAVE THIS BUILDING UNTIL IT CLEARS — IT'S TOO DANGEROUS!

HMM! WE MAY HAVE TO STAY IN ALL NIGHT!

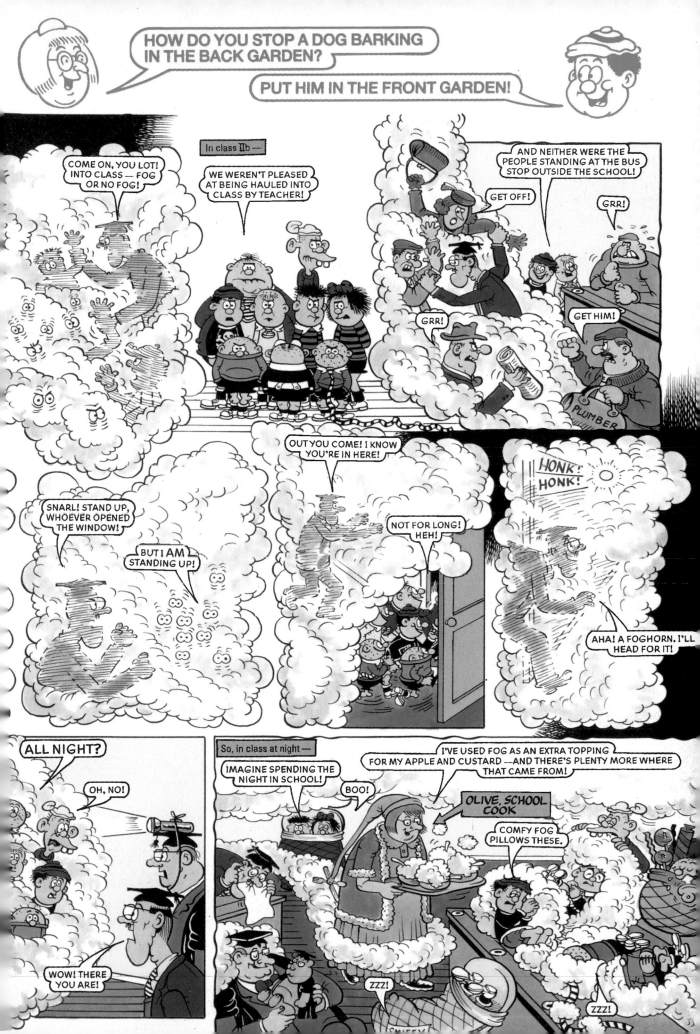

WHAT DO YOU CALL A LAUGHING MOTORBIKE?

A YAMAHA-HA!

TOUGH ON TEACHER

HUH! ISN'T TEACHER SOFT?

YES! NOT TOUGH AT ALL!

WHAT A SAP!

EH? ME? SOFT?

DOWN!

OH!

BOUN...

HO-HO! WELL, YOU LOOK TOUGHER NOW!

GRRRRR!

HEH-HEH!

YOU NEED SOME WEIGHT LIFTING NOW!

CHOMP! GUZZLE!

BUT WE DON'T HAVE ANY WEIGHTS, DANNY!

YOU'RE READY FOR A TEST OF STRENGTH NOW!

EH? WHAT?

OO...ER!

LET'S SEE IF YOU'RE TOUGH ENOUGH TO PICK UP THE LAST BISCUIT!

HEAD'S STUDY

THE LAST BICCY!

HOI! I'LL HAVE THAT BISCUIT, HEADFACE!

WOW! HOW TOUGH!

SWOON!

WHAT DO YOU GET IF YOU CROSS A PHONE WITH A FACE CLOTH?

SOMETHING THAT IS ALWAYS RINGING WET!

JEST NOT CRICKET

SCHOOL

ZOOM

BASH ST.

COUGH! COUGH!

SPLUTTER!

RATTLE

AW! SHAME! LOOK AT POOR OLD BERTIE, THE LOLLIPOP MAN!

COUGH! COUGH!

SCHOOL

BASH ST. SCHOOL

LEAP

PTCHEEE

ZOOM

THUMP

PHOOT

DOH!

WHERE ARE THE KIDS? HUMPH! ONLY MY PRIZE PUPIL, CUTHBERT HAS ARRIVED!

Shortly —

I'M BACK, SIR! READY TO FIGHT ANOTHER DAY!

ER ...I'D BETTER TEST YOUR VISION FIRST!

READ THIS PACKET!

EASY — 'CUSTARD CREAMS'! SEE — PERFECT EYESIGHT!

WAIT! SINCE YOUR EYESIGHT'S OKAY ...

CLASS IIB

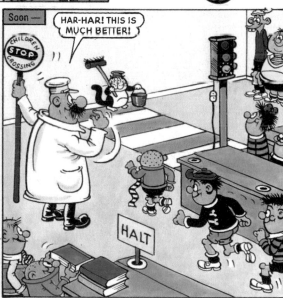

WHAT CLOTHES DO SNAILS WEAR?

SHELL SUITS!

SHADOW CHANCERS

WE HATE SCHOOL!

RAZZ

LISTEN — I HAVE AN IDEA . . . WHY DON'T WE JUST NOT GO TO SCHOOL TODAY?

ARE YOU FEELING OKAY, SMIFFY? THAT SOUNDS LIKE A GREAT IDEA!

PULSE

WAHEY! NO SCHOOL FOR US!

ZOOM ZOOM

I DON'T KNOW WHY WE DIDN'T THINK OF THIS BEFORE!

Next —

READY FOR MY SHOT?

ULP! THAT CAN'T BE . . .

MISS

. . . IT IS! BIG BERYL!

The kids are making shadows on the wall!

TO SCHOOL

TO SCHOOL

SCHOOL

OOF!

BASH ST. SCHOOL

BASH ST. SCHOOL

CRASH

HEH-HEH-HEH!

SNARL! NO ONE LAUGHS AT THE BASH STREET KIDS!

BIG OR NOT — WE'LL NOT STAND FOR IT!

LET'S GET BIG BERYL!

WHY DOES THE OCEAN ROAR?

BECAUSE IT'S GOT LOBSTERS CRAWLING ON ITS BED!

Soon—

SUPER!

Suddenly —

WAA! IT'S BIG BERYL — THE EDUCATION WELFARE OFFICER! NOW I REMEMBER WHY WE NEVER JUST 'DIDN'T GO' TO SCHOOL BEFORE!

WHAT'S AN EDUCATION . . . ER . . . EDUCATION WELCOME . . . ER . . .

A KID CATCHER!

HEH-HEH!

Then —

WHO'S MAKING THAT SHADOW?

THAT'S GOOD!

WAA! IT'S BIG BERYL! BACK TO SCHOOL AT ONCE!

EH? SHE'S TINY!

LET'S GO! SHE'LL NEVER GET US TO RETURN TO SCHOOL!

OH, NO!

ZOOM

HELP! WAA!

HUH!

CHORTLE! YOU SPOKE TOO SOON, KIDS!

WHAP!

WHAT HAPPENED NEXT?

Find out on page 81

The DADDY OF THEM ALL

WE'D BETTER HURRY TO SCHOOL!

WE'RE LATE—AS USUAL!

TO BASH STREET SCHOOL

Then—

Smiffy's Dad.

EH?

Later—

SIGH! NO CHANCE OF US BEING ABLE TO COPY ANSWERS FROM SMIFFY'S DAD!

HE'S JUST AS DIM AS HIS SON!

HUH! MY PENCIL'S BLUNT!

SCRAPE

DRING DRING

BREAK-TIME!

GOOD!

CLAP

THROW

I LIKE A CUP OF COFFEE AT TEA-BREAK!

YAHOO!

STAFF ROOM

ZOOM

THERE WAS A BIT OF A MIX UP THIS MORNING. SMIFFY'S GONE TO WORK IN MY PLACE!

AND WHAT WORK IS THAT?

CRASH

ER... DEMOLITION CRANE DRIVER!

WHAT'S ALWAYS BEHIND THE TIME?

THE BACK OF A CLOCK!

WHAT ARE YOU DOING COMING TO SCHOOL, SMIFFY'S DAD?

EH? SCHOOL! OH . . . A SIMPLE MISTAKE! SMIFFY AND I MUST HAVE GOT A BIT MIXED UP THIS MORNING! HE MUST HAVE GONE TO WORK IN PLACE OF ME! OOOER!

VERY SILLY MAN.

I MAY AS WELL JOIN YOU ANYWAY, KIDS!

HOWL!

CRUNCH

OO . . . OW! HAVEN'T YOU GROWN AND PUT ON WEIGHT SINCE YESTERDAY, SMIFFY?

ER . . . WELL . . . MISS . . .

HOP HOP

the Staff Room

HO-HO! LOOK! THAT'S THE HEAD'S MUG AND PAPER!

SMIFFY'S DAD WILL BE FOR IT!

RACING NEWS

BICCI

TEA

Sure enough.

YOU BOY! WHAT DO YOU THINK YOU'RE DOING?

PUSH

GLOOF!

WAIT A MINUTE YOU'RE NOT SMIFFY!

ER . . . WELL!

YOU'RE SMIFFY'S DAD!

The Artist has been as daft as Smiffy. Can you spot the deliberate mistake on this page? Answer on foot of page 19.

HO-HO! A SIMPLE MIX UP! NO HARM DONE!

SWING

THE REST OF THE DAY OFF FOR US! HA-HA!

CHUG A-LUG

LET'S GO!

SNORE AWAY SUCCESS

ZZZZZ
ZZZZZ
ZZZZZ

THE SQUARE ROOT OF THE BATTLE OF HASTINGS EQUALS THE . . .

IS MY LESSON BORING YOU?

Cuthbert, the class swot!

BOO-HOO!

IF WE CAN'T SLEEP — WE'RE LEAVING!

YEAH!

CLASS IIB

MY BOOK HAS GOT A SOLUTION TO YOU LOT RUNNING OFF TOO!

SPLAT!

KICK!

TIE!

EH!

Then —

MAYBE NOT . . .

RUMBLE!

. . . BUT WE MAKE A GREAT BATTERING RAM LIKE THIS!

PONK!

CRASH!

ZOOM!

I KNOW JUST THE MAN TO SEND THEM BACK!

ZOOM!

. . . NO PROBLEM! HOOTS! OKAY, TEACHER!

HERE WE GO!

HOW DOES A FARMER COUNT HIS COWS?

WITH A COWCULATOR!

NO, SIR! I CAN'T HEAR YOU FOR THIS LOT SNORING!

GRUNT!

SNORE!

RAZZZ!

WHEEZE!

AHA! THIS BOOK HAS A CURE FOR SNORING IN IT!

PEOPLE SNORE WHEN THEY SLEEP ON THEIR BACKS. THIS'LL WAKE THEM UP IF THEY DO THAT!

WHAT?

EH?

HOI!

SEW!

JAB!

HAT OW?

BAH! WE CAN'T GET THROUGH THE DOORWAY!

CLUNK!

CLUNK!

BUT THESE PLANKS ARE GOOD FOR PLAYING AT HELICOPTERS!

WAA! I MUST STOP THIS!

WHIRR!

BZZZT!

BREEZE!

EXAM PAPERS

THEY CAN'T CAUSE ANY TROUBLE LIKE THIS!

TIE!

ASH REET GGIS ORE

HAGGIS STORE

THERE WE'VE BEEN!

BOYLP!

PORRIDGE

SPLURP!

Soon—

HAGGIS STORE

WAH! WE'RE STUCK!

SPLUGE!

GLOOP!

WHEE EEE!

THROW

HOO-OOCH!

HA-HA! THE PERFECT CABER TOSS FROM HAMISH! WELCOME BACK, KIDS!

DONK!

THUD!

OH DEAR! I MUST . . .

RUMBLE

TRAMPLE

. . . AVOID THE MOB! WAA!

ZOOM

WALK? NO WAY, MATE!

PULL

I'LL GIVE YOU A LIFT! HA-HA!

LEAP

YAHOO!

WA

HOP PYOING!

PYO

HEH-HEH! THIS IS MUCH BETTER FOR A 'DOWN UNDER' LAD!

G . . . GASP!

CREAK CREAK

EVEN IF YOU ARE FROM THE OTHER SIDE OF THE WORLD — COME DOWN, AT ONCE!

Suddenly —

PLOP

DOOF!

CRASH

OOPS! NASTY!

WHY IS SMIFFY A USELESS HITCH-HIKER?

HE ALWAYS LEAVES EARLY TO AVOID THE TRAFFIC!

WHAT'S AN ALIEN'S FAVOURITE SWEETS?

MARTIAN MALLOWS!

PIN-BALL WIZARDS

3...2...1...

OO...ER!

CRASH!

BANG!

THUMP!

SHAKE

IIB

...GO!

CLASS IIB

SIT DOWN! SIT DOWN!

THUD!

THUNK!

ZOOM

IT'S ALL MADE OF RUBBER! CHUCKLE! IT'LL BEND — NOT BREAK!

GREAT! WE'LL TEST IT OKAY!

BEND

BEND

COO! IT HOLDS MORE NOSH THAN A WOODEN DESK!

BEND

BEND

But —

OH, NO!

POP

WELL, I SHALL PUT THE SUMS UP HERE. WE'LL GO THROUGH THEM TOGETHER!

AW!

NO!

−5 =
+7

LISTEN, KIDS. HERE'S WHAT TO DO . . .

RUBBER WORLD

OOF!

THUMP!

BYOING!

WHAT DO YOU GET IF YOU CROSS A SHIP WITH A RUBBISH CONTAINER?

A BIN LINER!

HO-HO! WHERE? NO DESKS LEFT, SIR!

AHEM!

AHA! IT'S OKAY!

THIS IS PERFECT FOR AN EDUCATION DEPARTMENT TEST! LEAVE IT TO ME. YOU'LL HAVE NEW CLASS FURNITURE SHORTLY!

PHEW!

Very soon —

HERE'S A NEW TYPE OF FURNITURE TO TEST!

CHORTLE!

CATCH!

JELLY BABIES

PYOINNNG!

Later —

OKAY — DO THE SUMS ON PAGE 14!

WE CAN'T, SIR!

RUBBER PENCILS CAN'T WRITE ON RUBBER JOTTERS!

BYOING! BOING!

HUMPH!

SNARL! WHO DID THAT?

HERE COMES TEACHER! NOW FOR PART TWO OF THE PLAN!

Shortly —

18 . . . 21 . . . 24 . . . 27 . . . 33 . . .

WELL I NEVER! NOW THEY'RE COUNTING! I MUST LOOK IN ON THE CLASS DURING THEIR MATHS LESSON!

CLASS IIB

. . . 35 . . . YAHOO!

HO-HO! WE JUST HAD TO PUSH OUR RUBBER DESKS ON THEIR SIDES TO MAKE THIS GIANT PIN-BALL GAME!

BONUS

BYOING

HEH-HEH!

BYOING

BOUNCE BOUNCE

3

3

3

WAH!

SIGH! I SHOULD HAVE KNOWN!

WHAT DO YOU GET IF YOU CROSS A PARROT WITH A WOODPECKER?

A BIRD THAT TELLS KNOCK-KNOCK JOKES!

ZOOM!

NECK TIES!

HELLO! 'BYE!

It looks as if Smiffy's Mum got it wrong!

In class IIB.

WE CAN'T LEAVE OUR SCARVES LYING ABOUT...

THROW!

TUG!

...TEACHER MIGHT TRIP OVER THEM!

SPLAT!

LOOSEN! ZIP! LOOSEN! ZIP!

OH, NO! NONE OF US ARE GOOD ENOUGH SCOUTS TO TIE PROPER KNOTS!

SLOO!

Suddenly —

CRASH!

NEVER MIND, SIR. WITH ALL THESE SCARVES AND BITS OF WOOD...

SLOO!

DOH!

TUG!

...ut in the playground...

WAIT A MINUTE...

...IT'S FREEZING OUT HERE WITHOUT OUR SCARVES!

SHAKE!

HEH-HEH! I CAN'T HEAR ANYONE KNOCKING WITH THIS SCARF OVER MY EARS! CHORTLE!

KNOCK! KNOCK!

TEA BICCIE

HERE'S THE TROPHY!

CLASS IIB

WAA!

...I'LL LAY OUT A COURSE INDOORS! WE'LL PLAY INSIDE THE SCHOOL BUILDINGS!

GREAT! SMASHING!

1ST. GREEN THIS WAY

GOOD SHOT, SIR!

HUMPH!

YEUCH!

FRYING PAN

WHERE'S THE 18th HOLE?

WE HAVEN'T SEEN THE GREEN AT ALL!

17TH GREEN

AHA! THERE IT IS!

18TH GREEN THIS WAY

HEADS STUDY

GOOD!

EH? HO!

18TH GREEN THIS WAY

HEADS STUDY

WHAT ARTIST SITS ON ICE CUBES?

BOTTY-CHILLY!

AHEM! THE BASH STREET GOLF TROPHY!

WE'RE READY TO COMPETE FOR IT, SIR!

PONK

WHAP

I'LL PHONE THE GOLF COURSE TO BOOK A TIME FOR OUR COMPETITION!

STARTER'S BOX

SORRY! COURSE CLOSED DUE TO FLOODING!

HMM! WHERE CAN WE PLAY, HEAD?

I KNOW . . .

NONK

BEND

DON'T DIRTY MY CUSTARD TOO MUCH WITH YOUR FEET — I STILL HAVE TO FINISH FRYING IT FOR LUNCH!

BAH!

WOBBLE

ER . . . TWO . . . AHEM . . . SIX!

SWISH

9TH TEE

HE MEANS — 'FORE'!

CRASH

TINKLE

SSSWISH

BZZZZ

WATCH IT, 'ERBERT!

In the Head's Study —

HA-HA! THE 18th GREEN'S IN HERE!

PRIVATE

18

YAHOO! HOLED MY PUTT FOR A ROUND OF 69! I CAN'T BE BEATEN BECAUSE THE REST CAN'T FINISH THEIR ROUNDS!

PRIVATE

GRRRR!

PUTT

PLOP

SLOO! I'M THE CHAMPION! CHORTLE!

CRUNCH BITE

SNARL!

CHEAT!

FILLED WITH TEA

THIS IS WHAT HAPPENED NEXT?

WHY IS A CLOCK DIRTY?

BECAUSE IT NEVER WASHES ITS HANDS OR FACE!

... HAVE TO FEED MY PETS! HA-HA!

WHAT A CHEEKY INTERRUPTION!

MOO! CHOMP!

LAP LAP

MILK

MUNCH MUNCH

HMM! THIS MUST BE A STRAY PIG! I DON'T REMEMBER BRINGING HIM ALONG!

CHOMP! OINK!

Soon —

1 + 1 =

SNAP SNAP

SIR-SIR!

DELIVERY FOR ...

SHOVE

... MISTER FATTY!

CHOMP! MUNCH! MID-MORNING SNACK! CHOMP!

WHIR

WHIRR

I'M FED UP WITH SILLY INTERRUPTIONS! I CAN'T GET ON AT ALL!

MUNCH! CHOMP!

TUG

OO ... AHEM!

TREMBLE

CLASS IIB

BIFF!

THUMP!

WALLOP

HA-HA-HA!

HUH! THAT'LL TEACH HIM TO BE SO RUDE!

CLASS IIB

CHORTLE! WE COULD HAVE TOLD TEACHER HIS WIFE WAS ARRIVING — BUT WE DIDN'T WANT TO INTERRUPT.

WHERE DO BEES COME FROM?

STINGAPORE!

DRIVEN CRAZY

At the Town Hall —

I'VE ENTERED THE KIDS FOR THIS COMPETITION!

BRAINY YOUNG ENGINEERS CONTEST →

EH? HOW ARE WE MEANT TO DO THAT?

TASK ONE
MAKE AN ADDI
MACHINE FRO
THE HALF DOZE
EGGS AND
FORTY DRINKI
STRAWS PROVIDE

LET'S CHANGE THE RULES OF THIS COMPETITION. IT'S BORING!

TASK ONE

RUB RUB

HOW UNUSUAL!

MAKE A CAR FROM YOUR TEACHER AND SOME OLD SCHOOL MEALS

FATTY WILL PROVIDE THE OLD SCHOOL MEALS — HE ALWAYS CARRIES SOME ABOUT WITH HIM!

FATTY'S SCHOOL BAG

SHAKE

THIS CUSTARD IS INEDIBLE!

WAH! GET ME AWAY FROM THAT THING!

FRANTIC SPINNING

SMIFFY!

TURN

EEK!

SPIN

ZOOM

CRUNCH

YOU'RE THE ONLY TEAM WITH A CAR LEFT — SO YOU WIN! OO — YAH!

EH?

JUDGE

ENTRANT 11

FLATTEN

CRUNCH

1ST PR

HAVE YOU GOT A PROBLEM, PAL?

Dear Plug,
I'm a teacher with a very unruly class. I constantly give them lines which all come back in the same handwriting. How can this be?
Yours in bewilderment,
Teacher

Dear Plug,
I have painful writer's cramp but I, er, can't tell you how I got it. What can I do?
Yours swottily
Cuthbert

Dear Teacher,
I suspect Cuthbert's doing their lines for them. Give them RAILWAY LINES in future. They'll all be too tired for mischief after that.
Yours helpfully, PLUG

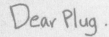

Dear Cuthbert,
Next time your class gets lines volunteer to carry teacher's case for him. Then it's HARD LINE on the rest of them.
Yours sneakily, PLUG

RAZZ!

Dear Plug,
I suffer ever so slightly from spots. My mum says I'll grow out of them. Is this true?
Yours on the spot,
Spotty

Dear Spotty,
Plant each of your feet in a large spotted flower pot full of compost. You'll definitely 'GROW OUT OF THEM'!
Yours spot-on.
Plug

COMPOST

Dear Plug.
Boo-Hoo! I've got a big fat belly. Should I diet?
Yours blubberingly
Fatty

Dear Fatty.
You could lie on your back in your swimming trunks, DYE IT grey and call it MOUNT OLIVE. After all it's Olive's cooking that's to blame for your belly.
Yours chubbily
Plug

MT. OLIVE

Dear Plug.
I'm the only girl in my class and all the boys are SO UGLY. I don't fancy any of them. Any suggestions?
Yours, not in love, Toots

Dear Toots.
I take it you don't mean ME! Anyway just count yourself lucky Fatty hasn't got a CRUSH on you.
Yours lightheartedly, Plug

Dear Plug.
I'm fed-up having to stand in the corner for misbehaving. My legs go all stiff and it's dead boring.
Yours in a corner.
'Erbert.

Dear 'Erbert.
Ask to be put in the school round tower. When Teacher tells you to stand in the corner you'll walk for miles. Yours toweringly, Plug

SCHOOL ROUND TOWER

Dear Plug.
I'm fed up collecting litter dropped in the playground by the Bash Street Kids. What can I do?
Yours litterally,
The Janitor.

Dear Janitor.
Turn the school into a boarding school by BOARDING UP the tuck shop door. That should solve it.
Yours not so litterally,
Plug

BANG!

THUD!

TUCK SHOP

CHOC   TOFFEE

At Teacher's house —

WAIT — I'LL HELP!

EH?

I WAS AN OLD SCOUT LEADER. WE'LL FORM OUR OWN TROOP!

ZONK

OKAY!

In the country —

RUBBING TWO STICKS TOGETHER IS A WAY TO START A FIRE!

RUB RUB

RUB RUB

OOH! HOW DOES THAT WORK?

SCRATCH

CRACKLE

HA-HA! SMIFFY'S HEAD IS A BETTER WAY!

YUM!

ERK!

TUG

SIZZLE

ER . . . WELL . . . AHEM! I KNOW, WE'LL TRACK SOMETHING FOR OUR SUPPER!

CHOMP! GUZZLE!

ZOOM

GRRR!

Soon —

WOW! THE UNMISTAKEABLE PRINTS OF A POT-BELLIED WART HOG!

ISN'T TEACHER GOOD AT TRACKING?

SNARL! YES! FIRST CLASS! GRRR!

BITE

CRUNCH

CHIRP

ZONK

PLUG

SLOOP!

HEH-HEH! CHOMP!

TUG

TEACHER'S TENT

'ERBERT'S TENT

SPOTTY

SMIFFY'S TENT (UPSIDE DOWN)

CHOMP

WILFRID

FATTY'S TENT

HOT

CHOMP

DANNY'S TENT

WHO WROTE A BOOK ABOUT POULTRY?

CHARLES CHICKENS!

HELLO, READERS! ART CLASS TODAY. I'VE ASKED THE KIDS TO BRING SOMETHING ALONG WITH THEM TO PAINT. THE BEST PAINTING WILL BE PRINTED IN THE LAST FRAME OF THESE PAGES AS A PRESENT FOR YOU! ISN'T THAT EXCITING?

CRASH

OOF! WHAT NOW?

BUMP!

SHAKE!

HO-HO! BROUGHT ALONG A STUFFED TIGER, SIDNEY! VERY GOOD!

PAT! PAT!

NO — HE'S REAL! ONE OF MY PETS. BUT HE COULD SOON BE STUFFED . . .

EEK!

SCRAPE

R-ROAR!

SO DID I! THAT'S WHY I'M WORKING ON THIS SPECIAL CANVAS!

HO-HO! READY CRACKED!

DROOL! ALL OF THIS PAINTING HAS MADE ME HUNGRY — SO I'LL EAT MY 'STILL LIFE' PROP!

LIFT!

CHOMP! GUZZLE!

HOI!

SQUASH!

SPLUDGE!

GRR!

WAA!

SPLURT!

WOW!

RUMBLE!

WAA!

CRASH!

HI, TEACHER. MY UNCLE BERT BROUGHT MY BACK GARDEN ON HIS TRUCK FOR ME TO PAINT!

OO . . . SILLY BOY!

. . . WITH 'TEACHER'! IF HE CATCHES HIM!

HELP! NICE KITTY!

ZOOM!

Later —

WHAT HAVE YOU BROUGHT TO PAINT?

LOOK — A MIRROR! I'M GOING TO DO A SELF PORTRAIT!

EASEL

TITTER! I KNEW THAT WOULD HAPPEN!

SMASH!

ER . . . READERS, I'M AFRAID THERE ISN'T A 'BEST PAINTING' TO PUT INTO THE LAST FRAME. YOU'LL JUST HAVE TO MAKE DO WITH ONE ENTITLED — 'ARTISTS AT WORK'!